Little Sticker Dolly Dressing
Puppies

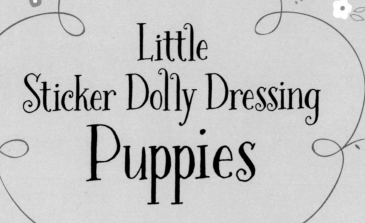

Written by Fiona Watt
Illustrated by Lizzie Mackay
Designed by Jodie Smith

Contents

A new puppy

Tilly is choosing a new puppy. She's looking for a friendly one that likes to play. She's finding it so difficult to decide which puppy she likes best.

In the park

Every morning Emily and Keira take their puppies for a walk in the local park. They all love to play together. Other puppies often scamper over to join in the fun.

Emily

Keira

5

Lara

Coco

Winter walk

Lara and Ruby woke this morning to find the ground covered in snow. They put on their winter clothes and boots, then dressed their puppies in coats to keep them warm, too.

Ruby

Ozzie

7

Holly

Grooming salon

Holly and Alice work at a grooming salon where owners bring their puppies to be washed and have their fur and claws trimmed. Some puppies love the attention, but others aren't quite so happy.

Alice

Natalie

Elena

Puppy school

Once a week, Natalie and Elena take their puppies, Mitzy and Max, to a training class. The puppies have learned how to sit and stay, and come when their names are called.

On the beach

It's a warm, sunny day. Alyssa and Paige are playing with their puppies on the beach. The puppies were a little scared of the waves to begin with, but now love running around and splashing in the sea.

Alyssa

Paige

13

It's raining

The dolls go for a walk every morning and afternoon whatever the weather. The puppies, dressed in raincoats, don't seem to worry about the rain or the puddles.

Jasmine

Bertie

Izzy

Molly

15

Bonnie

Visiting the vet

Bonnie has brought her puppies to see the vet. Skye hurt her leg chasing Luna around the park. Anika has cleaned her leg and wrapped a bandage around it.

Anika

Ellie

Playing games

Most puppies love to play with balls and chew things. Ellie
and Maya are playing with the puppies, but they're making
sure each puppy doesn't get too tired or overexcited.

Maya

19

Puppy party

It's Cassie's birthday and she's having a puppy-themed party. She's invited all her friends to the party and has told them to bring their puppies, too.

Megan

Jessie

Bursting bubbles

Megan is blowing bubbles with a special pet-safe
bubble mixture. Her dog Amber and Honey the puppy
are jumping around with Jessie, trying to catch them.

Sleepy puppies

Ssshhhhhh! Don't wake the little puppies.
They're tired out after an exciting, fun day.

In the park
Pages 4-5

Put Emily's top on first

Emily's clothes

Keira's outfit

Winter walk
Pages 6-7

Put Lara's gloves
on before her coat

Coco's
coat

Lara's
outfit

Ruby's outfit

Ozzie's
coat

Grooming salon

Pages 8-9

Holly's clothes

Alice's clothes

Puppy school
Pages 10-11

Max

Natalie's clothes

Elena's clothes

Mitzy

Visiting the vet
Pages 16-17

Bonnie's clothes

Luna

Anika's uniform

Skye

Playing games
Pages 18-19

Ellie's clothes

Maya's outfit